MUSICIANSHIP FOR THE OLDER BEGINNER ORGANIST

by James Bastien
CONSULTANT: Ivyle Lederer

The Bastien Older Beginner Organ Library

PREFACE

MUSICIANSHIP FOR THE OLDER BEGINNER ORGANIST is designed to be used as a companion book to **THE OLDER BEGINNER ORGAN COURSE. Theory, Technic,** and **Sight Reading** materials are correlated unit by unit to the basic course. It may also be used with any other organ course.

The **Theory** portion contains a combination of written exercises and keyboard harmony.

The **Technic** portion contains manual and pedal exercises to develop proficiency in basic skills. When playing the exercises in the **Technic** and **Theory** portions, the student may use any combinations or solo stops without using any tremolo or vibrato.

The **Sight Reading** portion provides additional reading to reinforce new concepts. A variety of reading experiences is provided to relieve monotony. The registrations given are only suggestions; the student should consult the owner's manual for additional possibilities. Before playing, the student should give a brief pre-study analysis:

    1) tap or clap the rhythm;
    2) observe the clef, key, and time signature.

While playing, the student should:

    1) keep eyes on the music;
    2) look ahead;
    3) keep going.

This balanced program will provide the student with a thorough beginning music program in basic fundamentals.

Coordination of Materials with the OLDER BEGINNER ORGAN COURSE, LEVEL 1

Published by Kjos West.
Distributed by Neil A. Kjos Music Company.
National Order Desk, 4382 Jutland Dr., San Diego, CA 92117

ISBN 0-8497-5302-3

CONTENTS

UNIT 1

THEORY

WHITE KEY NAMES

1. Write the names of these white keys.

C MAJOR FIVE FINGER POSITION

2. Write the C Major Five Finger Position forward on this keyboard. Play this position on the organ in different places. Use either hand. Say the letters aloud as you play.

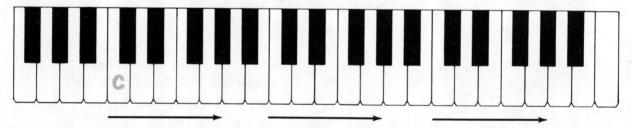

3. Write the C Major Five Finger Position backward on this keyboard. Play this position on the organ in different places. Use either hand. Say the letters aloud as you play.

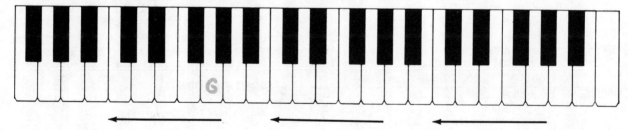

INTERVALS (2nds, 3rds)

The distance between two tones is called an INTERVAL. On the keyboard, neighbor white keys are a 2nd apart. Skipped white keys are a 3rd apart.

Examples of White Key Intervals

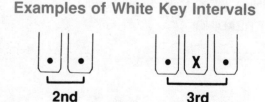

4. Play some intervals of 2nds and 3rds on the organ (on the manuals or pedals).

5. Write intervals of 2nds up or down from the given letters. Play these intervals on the organ (on the manuals or pedals).

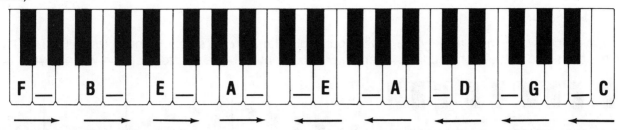

6. Write intervals of 3rds up or down from the given letters. Play these intervals on the organ (on the manuals or pedals).

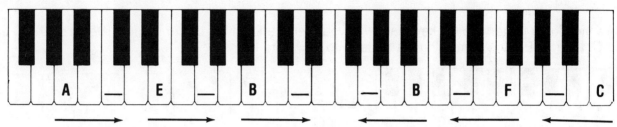

RHYTHM

Quarter Note	Half Note	Whole Note
♩	♩	o
1 beat	2 beats	4 beats

7. Clap and count this rhythm pattern.

8. Tap this rhythm pattern with both hands. Count aloud while tapping. The notes above the line are for your Right Hand; the notes below the line are for your Left Hand.

R.H.

L.H.

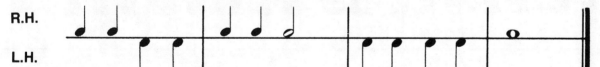

CHORDS AND PEDALS

9. Chords and pedals played together provide accompaniment (or harmony) for melodies. Play these chords and pedals in the rhythm given. (Observe the ties.)

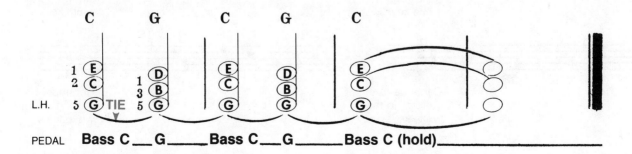

TECHNIC

FIVE-FINGER PATTERNS (Legato Touch)

1. Play this five-finger pattern up the keyboard with your Right Hand on the Upper manual. Use a LEGATO touch (smooth, connected). Begin on Middle C, then D, E, etc., continuing the pattern up the white keys.

2. Play this five-finger pattern up the keyboard with your Left Hand on the Lower manual. Begin on the C below Middle C, then D, E, etc., continuing the pattern up the white keys.

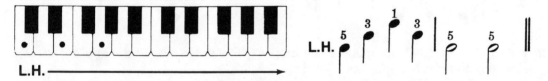

3. Play this pattern up the keyboard with your Right Hand on the Upper manual. Begin on Middle C, then D, E, etc., continuing the pattern up the white keys.

4. Play this pattern up the keyboard with your Left Hand on the Lower manual. Begin on the C below Middle C, then D, E, etc., continuing the pattern up the white keys.

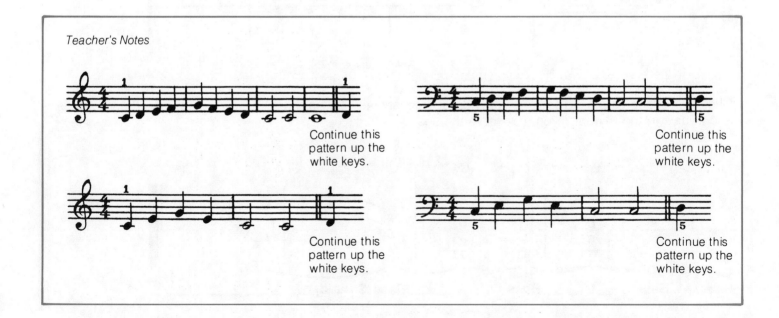

Teacher's Notes

Continue this pattern up the white keys.

Continue this pattern up the white keys.

Continue this pattern up the white keys.

Continue this pattern up the white keys.

SIGHT READING

PRACTICE DIRECTIONS
1. Clap and count the rhythm of the Right Hand melody aloud before playing.
2. Find your position for hands and feet on the manuals and pedals.
3. Watch the music while playing.
4. While playing, SING the Right Hand finger numbers aloud.
5. While playing again, COUNT the rhythm aloud.
6. While playing again, SING the letter names of the Right Hand notes aloud.

ELECTRONIC ORGANS
UPPER: Flutes 8' 4'
LOWER: Diapason 8'
PEDAL: 8' (Sustain On)
TREM: On (Fast)   VIB: Off

DRAWBAR ORGANS
UPPER: 00 8803 000
LOWER: (00) 6542 000
PEDAL: 4 3 Spinet 4 (Sustain On)
VIB: On (V2)

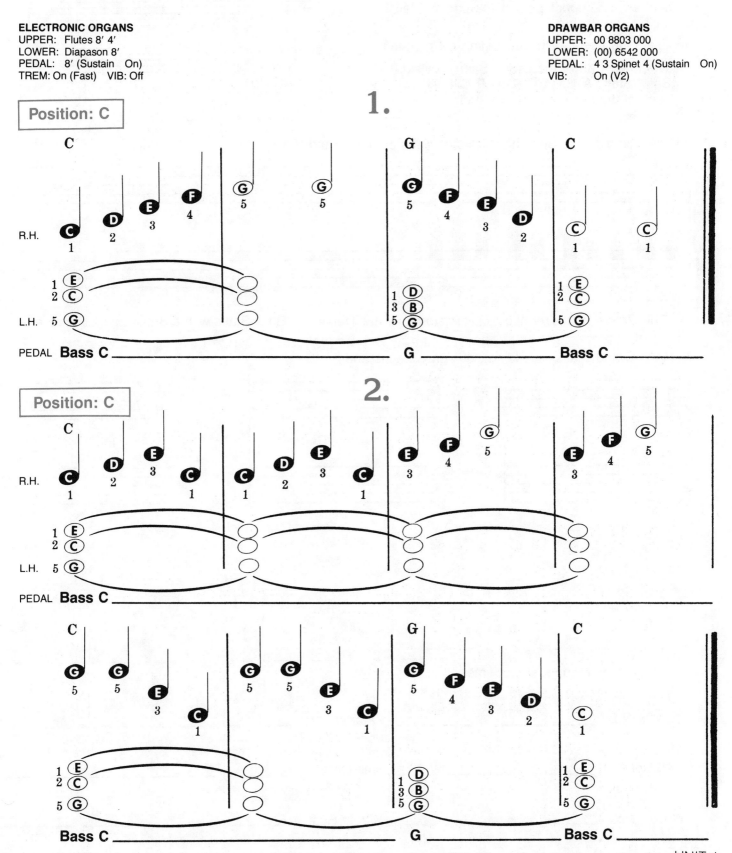

UNIT 2

THEORY

THE GRAND STAFF

Organ music is written on a GRAND STAFF which has two complete sets of lines and spaces. The upper part of the Grand Staff is called the Treble Staff. A Treble Clef or G Clef 𝄞 is used at the beginning of this staff.

The lower part of the Grand Staff is called the Bass Staff. A Bass Clef or F Clef sign 𝄢 is used at the beginning of this staff.

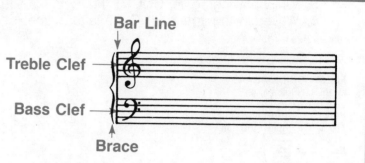

1. Draw some Treble Clef and Bass Clef signs on this Grand Staff.

The Grand Staff is formed by joining together the Treble and Bass Staffs with a Brace and a Bar Line.

2. Make Grand Staffs by adding clef signs, braces and bar lines.

NOTES AND RESTS

	Quarter	Half	Whole
Notes	♩	𝅗𝅥	𝅝
Rests	𝄽	𝄼	𝄻

3. Draw each note and rest four times.

Quarter Note _____ _____ _____ _____   Quarter Rest _____ _____ _____ _____

Half Note _____ _____ _____ _____   Half Rest _____ _____ _____ _____

Whole Note _____ _____ _____ _____   Whole Rest _____ _____ _____ _____

STEMMING NOTES

With the exception of the whole note, all notes have stems. Notes on or above the middle line of the staff have down stems; these stems are on the LEFT side of the notes. Notes below the middle line have up stems; these stems are on the RIGHT side of the notes.*

Down Stems   **Up Stems**

4. Draw stems on these note heads. Write the name of each note below it.

___ ___ ___ ___ ___   ___ ___ ___ ___ ___

*When organ music is written on two staffs, the left hand chords are written with up stems and the pedal part is written with down stems for ease in reading.

INTERVALS (through the 5th)

The distance in pitch between two notes is an INTERVAL. Note the similarity between 2nds and 4ths (line-space or space-line), and between 3rds and 5ths (line-line or space-space).

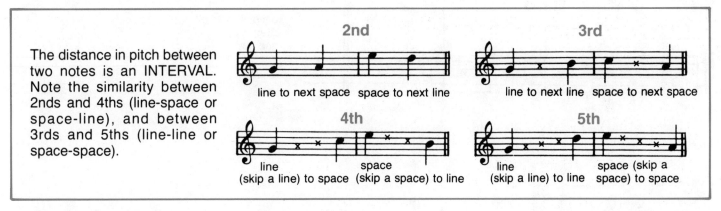

2nd
line to next space   space to next line

3rd
line to next line   space to next space

4th
line
(skip a line) to space   (skip a space) to line
space

5th
line
(skip a line) to line   space (skip a space) to space
space (skip a space) to space

5. Name these intervals.

3rd ___   ___   ___   ___   ___

6. Draw notes up or down from the given notes to form these intervals. Write the letter names of both notes on the blanks below. Play these intervals.

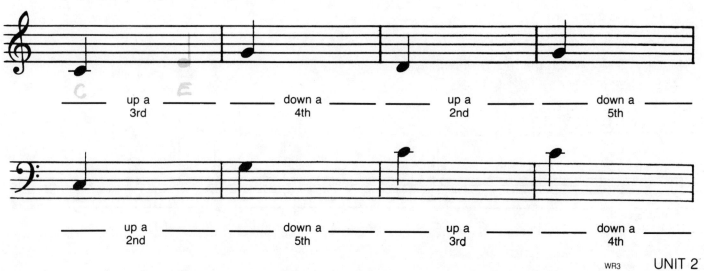

___ *C* ___ up a   ___ *E* ___ down a   ___ ___ up a   ___ ___ down a
3rd   4th   2nd   5th

___ ___ up a   ___ ___ down a   ___ ___ up a   ___ ___ down a
2nd   5th   3rd   4th

TECHNIC

FIVE-FINGER PATTERNS

Play hands separately at first. Use a legato touch. These exercises may be played on the Upper and Lower manuals; or BOTH HANDS may play on the Lower manual.

1.

Continue this pattern up the white keys.

2.

Continue this pattern up the white keys.

PEDALS

Play with the toe of your Left Foot. While playing, do not look at the pedals. Learn to judge intervals (distances between pedals) by "feel" and by listening to the tones.

3.

PEDAL

CHORDS AND PEDALS

Play by "feel." Watch the music while playing.

4.

LOWER

PEDAL

(hold pedal)

SIGHT READING

ELECTRONIC ORGANS
UPPER: Flute 8′ Reed 8′
LOWER: Diapason 8′
PEDAL: Flute 8′
TREM: On (Fast) VIB: On (Full)

DRAWBAR ORGANS
UPPER: 00 7856 321
LOWER: (00) 5443 111
PEDAL: 3 3 Spinet 4
VIB: On (V2)

FOLK SONG

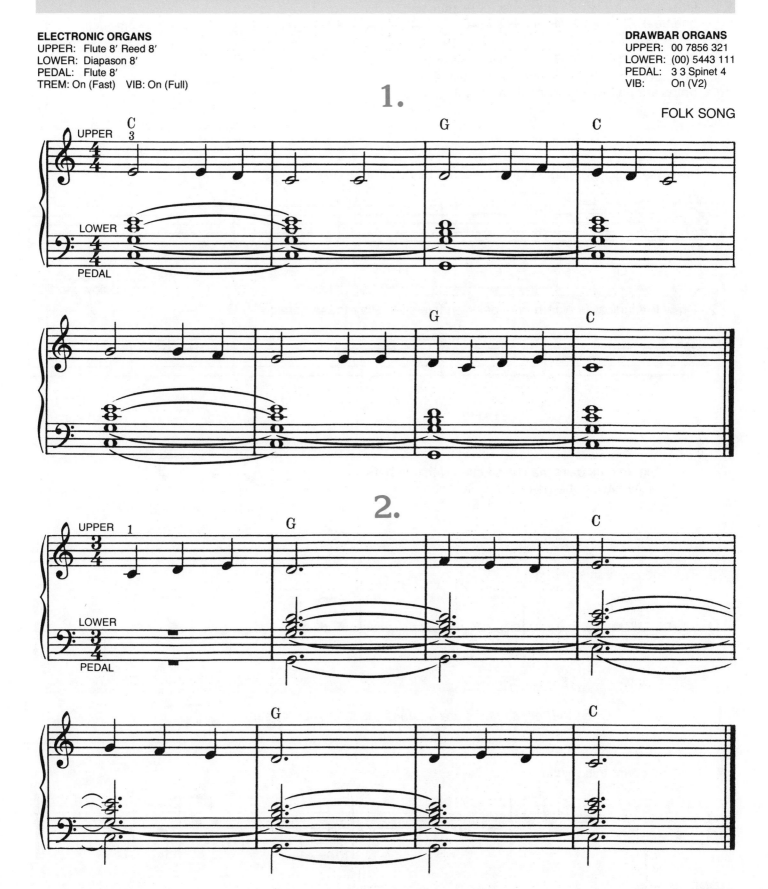

UNIT 3

THEORY

EIGHTH NOTES

An EIGHTH NOTE receives HALF a beat in a time signature where a quarter note receives one beat. One eighth note has a FLAG (♪).

TWO EIGHTH NOTES equal one quarter note and receive a total of one beat. Two eighth notes are paired together with a BEAM (⌐).

Eighth Note   **Eighth Rest**

♪ = 1/2 beat   ❼ = 1/2 beat

Two Eighth Notes

♫ = ♩ (1 beat)

1. Draw the indicated single eighth notes on this staff. Play these notes.

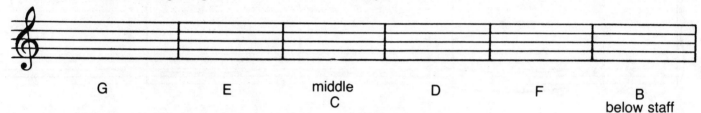

G   E   middle   D   F   B
                       C   below staff

2. Draw the indicated eighth note pairs on this staff. Play these notes.

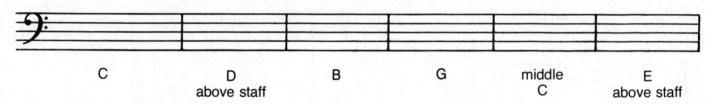

C   D   B   G   middle   E
        above staff   C   above staff

Eighth note pairs may be counted with numbers or by saying the note names in rhythm.

Count: 1   and   2   and   (etc.)
or
Count: two 8ths   two 8ths (etc.)

3. Tap and count this rhythm.

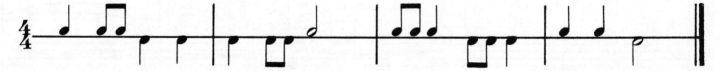

Often four eighth notes are grouped together with a beam: ♬

4. Tap and count this rhythm.

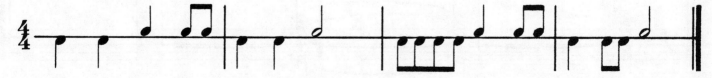

INTERVALS (through the 6th)

Two notes played together form a HARMONIC interval:

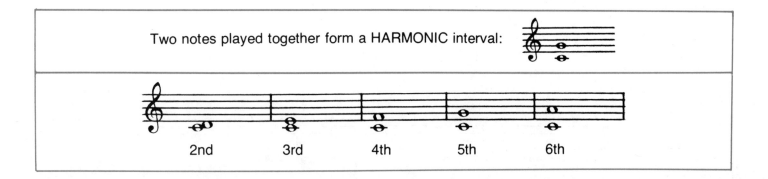

| 2nd | 3rd | 4th | 5th | 6th |

5. Name these harmonic intervals. Play them.

___ ___ ___ ___ ___ ___

Two notes played separately form a MELODIC interval:

6. Name these melodic intervals. Play them.

___ ___ ___ ___ ___ ___

CHORDS (C,F,G)

The three chords C, F, and G can be used to harmonize many melodies.

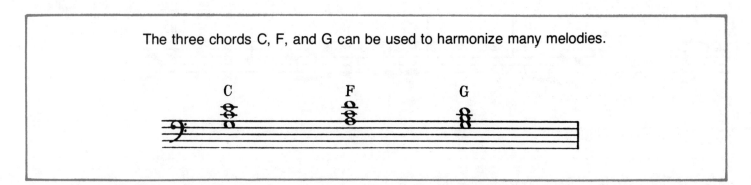

7. Draw the following chords. Use whole notes. Play these chords.

C   F   G   C

TECHNIC

5THS-6THS

Play by "feel." Do not look down at your hands for the stretch of the 6th.

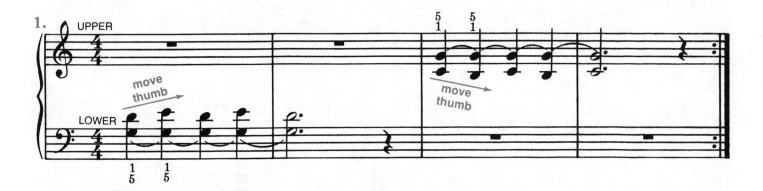

EIGHTH NOTES

Play hands separately at first. These exercises may be played on the Upper and Lower manuals; or BOTH HANDS may play on the Lower manual.

Continue this pattern up the white keys.

Continue this pattern up the white keys.

CHORDS AND PEDALS

Play by "feel." Watch the music while playing.

SIGHT READING

PRACTICE DIRECTIONS   Follow the same practice directions given on page 11.*

ELECTRONIC ORGANS
UPPER: Reed 16' Flutes 8' 4' 2'
LOWER: Diapason 8' Tibia 8'
PEDAL: 16' 8'
TREM: On (Slow/Chorale)

DRAWBAR ORGANS
UPPER: 42 8875 543
LOWER: (00) 5645 322
PEDAL: 5 4 Spinet 5
VIB: On (Chorus)

1.

ELECTRONIC ORGANS
UPPER: Banjo or Strings 8' 4'
LOWER: Tibia 8'
PEDAL: 16'
TREM. and VIB: Off

DRAWBAR ORGANS
UPPER: 00 3676 532 (Percussion On)
LOWER: (00) 5432 000
PEDAL: 4 4 Spinet 4
VIB: Off

2.

FOLK SONG

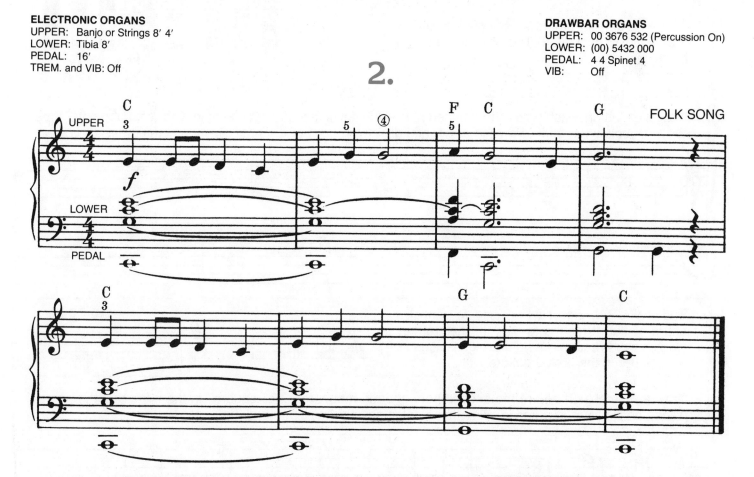

*Similar practice directions should be followed throughout this book for SIGHT READING portions.
**Notice that the Left Foot begins on Low C.

WR3   UNIT 3

UNIT 4

THEORY

ACCIDENTALS

	Sharp	Flat	Natural
ACCIDENTALS are added signs which temporarily alter the pitch of notes. The effect of accidental signs lasts only within the measure they appear.	♯	♭	♮

A SHARP sign (♯) before a note means to play the next key to the right. The next key may be black or white.

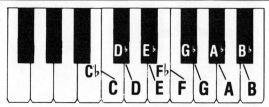

1. Draw a sharp before each note. The "square" in the middle of the sharp is placed on a line or in a space. Say the note names aloud as you play.

A FLAT sign (♭) before a note means to play the next key to the left. The next key may be black or white.

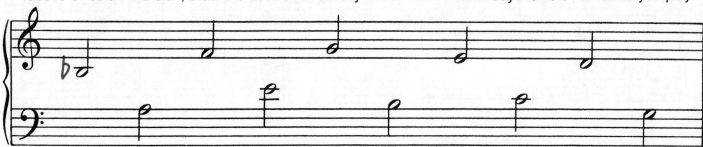

2. Draw a flat before each note. The rounded part of the flat is placed on a line or in a space. If the note appears above or below the staff, draw the accidental directly in front of the note. Say the note names as you play.

The NATURAL sign (♮) is used to cancel a sharp or flat. It means to play the natural key (white key). Frequently a natural sign is used as a reminder in the next measure.

3. Draw a natural sign before the second note in each measure. The "square" in the middle of the natural is placed on a line or in a space. Play these notes saying their names aloud.

G7 CHORD

The G7 chord is formed by adding F to the G chord.

4. Write four G7 chords on this staff.

HARMONIZING MELODIES

5. Write the harmony (chords and pedals) for these melodies. Choose a registration and write it in pencil. Play these pieces.

REGISTRATION
UPPER: _____
LOWER: _____
PEDAL: _____
TREM. or VIB: _____

Jingle Bells

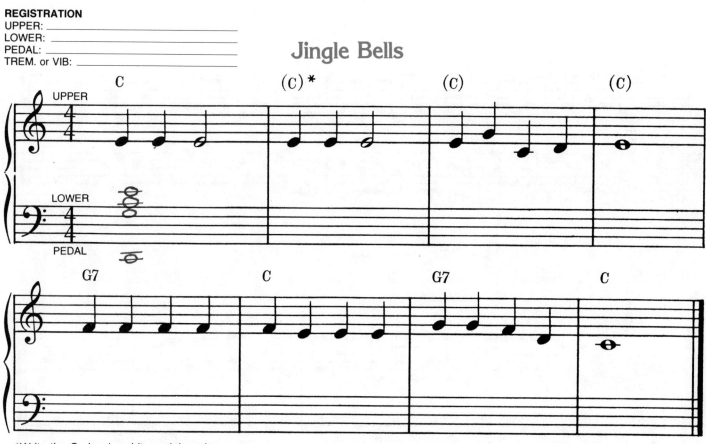

*Write the C chord and its pedal again.

REGISTRATION
UPPER: _____
LOWER: _____
PEDAL: _____
TREM. or VIB: _____

English Folk Song

TECHNIC

5THS-6THS

Play by "feel." Do not look down at your hands for the stretch of the 6th.

Continue this pattern up the white keys.

EIGHTH NOTES

Play hands separately at first. This exercise may be played on the Upper and Lower manuals; or BOTH HANDS may play on the Lower manual.

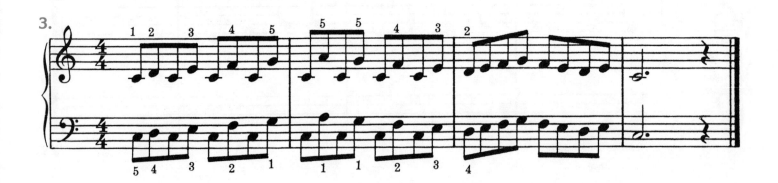

CHORDS AND PEDALS

Play by "feel." Watch the music while playing.

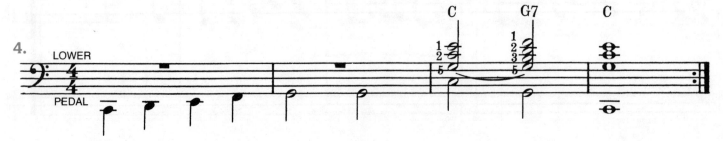

SIGHT READING

Choose a registration using flutes and strings and very slow tremolo or light vibrato. Write it in pencil.

REGISTRATION
UPPER: _____
LOWER: _____
PEDAL: _____
TREM. or VIB: _____

REGISTRATION
UPPER: _____
LOWER: _____
PEDAL: _____
TREM. or VIB: _____

UNIT 5

THEORY

HALF STEPS AND WHOLE STEPS

From one key to the nearest key with no key in between is a HALF STEP.

From one key to a neighbor key with one key in between is a WHOLE STEP.

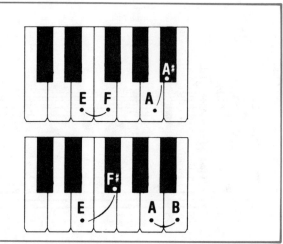

1. Write 1/2 for half step and 1 for whole step. Play these half and whole steps.

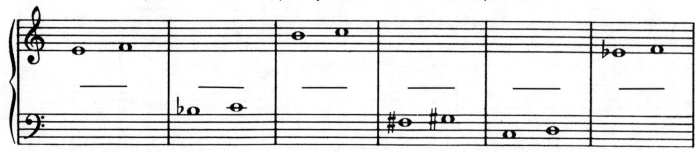

FORMATION OF MAJOR SCALES

There are eight tones in the Major scale. The tones are called SCALE DEGREES. The scale degrees are arranged in a pattern of whole steps and half steps. The first note in the scale is called the keynote.

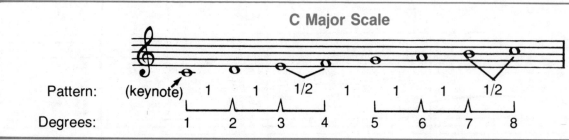

C Major Scale

Pattern:	(keynote)	1	1	1/2	1	1	1	1/2
Degrees:	1	2	3	4	5	6	7	8

2. Draw the notes of the C Major scale using whole notes. Mark the half steps with a ∨ . Write 1 for whole step and 1/2 for half step. Write in the fingering.* Play this scale first with your Right Hand, then with your Left Hand.

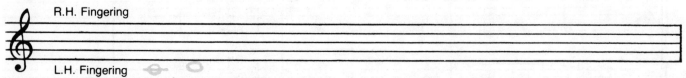

R.H. Fingering

L.H. Fingering

*See page 45 for the C Major scale fingering.

HARMONIZING LEAD LINES

> A LEAD LINE is the written melody of a song. No accompaniment is written. The organist must improvise (make up) the accompaniment. The chord symbols (shown above the melody) tell which chords and pedals to use in the accompaniment.

3. Play the following melodies with your Right Hand. Play chords and pedals indicated by the chord symbols. If no chord symbol is given in a measure, repeat (hold) the same chord from the measure before.

Good King Wenceslas

CHRISTMAS SONG

Polly Wolly Doodle

COLLEGE SONG

Old Folks at Home

STEPHEN FOSTER

TECHNIC

C MAJOR SCALE STUDIES

Practice these studies turning the thumb under or crossing over the thumb as smoothly as possible.

Contrary Motion

Parallel Motion

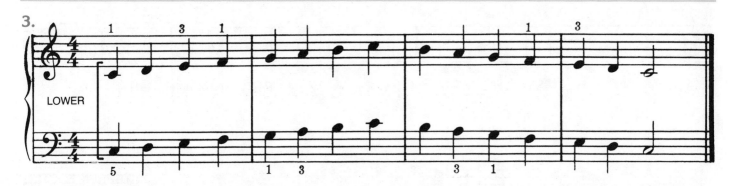

Watch the music while playing this pedal and chord study.

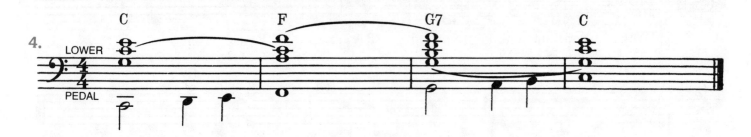

*Play BOTH HANDS on the Lower manual. These exercises may also be played on the Upper and Lower manuals.

SIGHT READING

ELECTRONIC ORGANS
UPPER: Reed 16' Flutes 8' 4' 2'
LOWER: Diapason 8' Tibia 8'
PEDAL: 16' 8'
TREM: On (Slow/Chorale)

DRAWBAR ORGANS
UPPER: 42 8875 543
LOWER: (00) 5645 322
PEDAL: 5 4 Spinet 5
VIB: On (Chorus)

JOY TO THE WORLD
(Handel)

1.

ELECTRONIC ORGANS
UPPER: Banjo or Strings 8' 4'
LOWER: Tibia 8'
PEDAL: 16'
TREM. and VIB: Off

DRAWBAR ORGANS
UPPER: 00 3676 532 (Percussion On)
LOWER: (00) 5432 000
PEDAL: 4 4 Spinet 4
VIB: Off

DIXIE
(Emmett)

2.

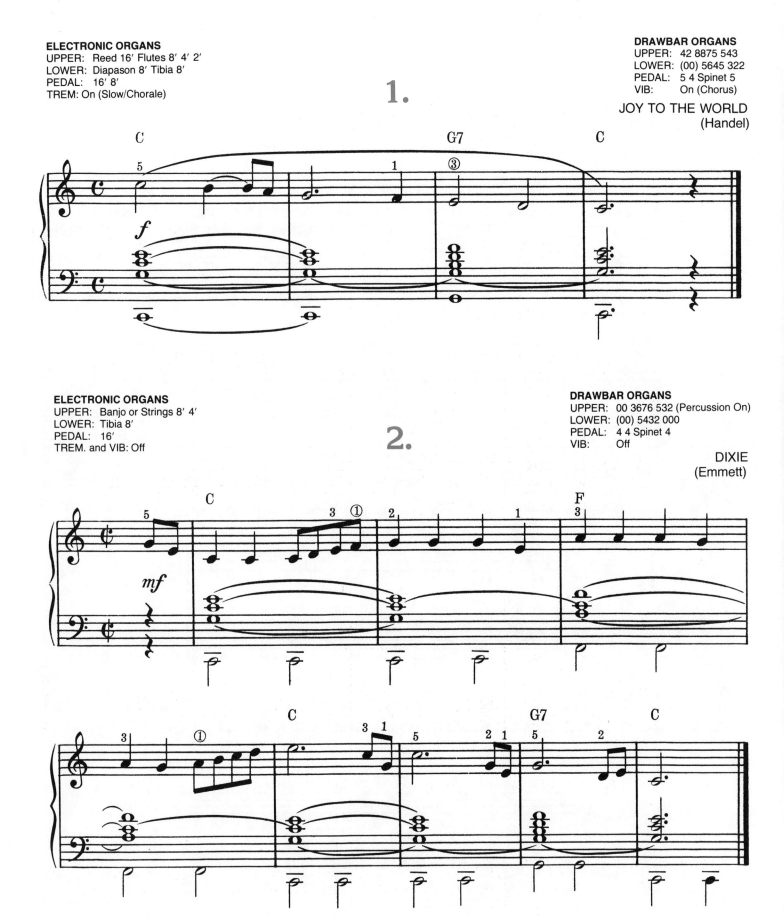

UNIT 6

THEORY

G MAJOR KEY SIGNATURE

The KEY SIGNATURE consists of the sharps or flats written at the beginning of each staff. (EXCEPTION: the key of C Major has NO sharps or flats.) These sharps or flats are to be played permanently throughout the piece.

SHARP KEY SIGNATURES of Major keys are identified by:

1. naming the last sharp   then,   2. naming the next letter in the musical alphabet (the name of the next note ABOVE the last sharp).

 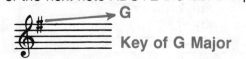

1. Write the G Major key signature after each clef sign.

G MAJOR FIVE FINGER POSITION

The G Major Five Finger Position is G - A - B - C - D.

2. Write the notes for this position in both clefs.* Use quarter notes. Play this position.

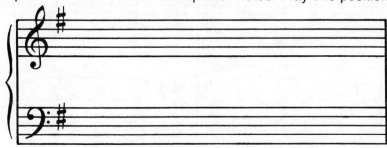

CHORDS (G, C, D7)

The three chords G, C, and D7 are used repeatedly in the key of G Major.

3. Draw the following chords. Use dotted half notes. Play these chords.

G   C   D7   G

*Refer to page 45 for the complete G Major scale. The manuscript paper on pages 46-48 may be used for practice in writing out this scale.

DOTTED QUARTER NOTE

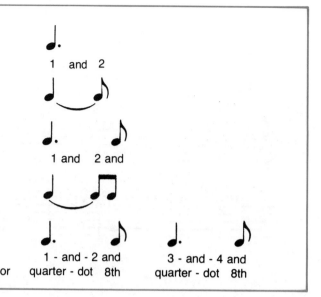

The DOTTED QUARTER NOTE receives 1½ beats:

It is the same as a quarter note tied to an eighth note:

The dotted quarter note is incomplete by itself (it cannot end on a ½ beat), and is usually written this way:

It is the same as:

This dotted rhythm pattern may be counted with numbers or by saying the note names in rhythm:

4. Tap and count this rhythm.

HARMONIZING MELODIES

5. Write the harmony (chords and pedals) for this melody. Play this piece.

ELECTRONIC ORGANS
UPPER: Flutes 8' 4'
LOWER: Diapason 8'
PEDAL: 8'
TREM: On (Fast)   VIB: Off

DRAWBAR ORGANS
UPPER: 00 8803 000
LOWER: (00) 6542 000
PEDAL: 4 3 Spinet 4
VIB: On (V2)

Away in a Manger

TECHNIC

G MAJOR SCALE STUDIES

Practice these studies turning the thumb under or crossing over the thumb as smoothly as possible.

Contrary Motion

Parallel Motion

Watch the music while playing this pedal and chord study.

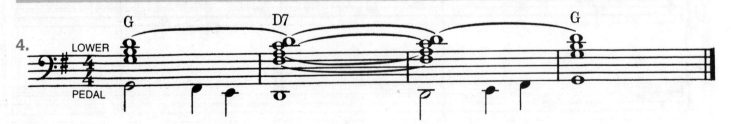

SIGHT READING

ELECTRONIC ORGANS
UPPER: Reed 16′ Flutes 8′ 4′ 2′
LOWER: Diapason 8′ String 8′
PEDAL: 16′ 8′
TREM: On (Slow/Chorale)   VIB: Off

DRAWBAR ORGANS
UPPER: 42 8875 543
LOWER: (00) 5645 322
PEDAL: 4 4 Spinet 5
VIB: On Chorus

1.

HYMN TUNE

ELECTRONIC ORGANS
Add Harp Sustain or String Sustain
to the Solo Manual; play with a
non-legato touch.

DRAWBAR ORGANS
Use Variable Sustain on the
Solo Manual; play with a
non-legato touch.

2.

AMARYLLIS
(Ghys)

UNIT 7

THEORY

F MAJOR KEY SIGNATURE

The key of F Major has one flat: B-flat. Play all the B's flat in a piece with an F Major key signature.

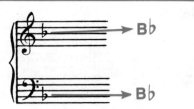

1. Write the F Major key signature after each clef sign.

2. Name the Major key shown by each key signature.

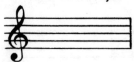 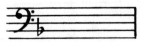  

_____   _____   _____   _____

F MAJOR FIVE FINGER POSITION

The F Major Five Finger Position is F - G - A - Bb - C.

3. Write the notes for this position in both clefs.* Use quarter notes. Play this position.

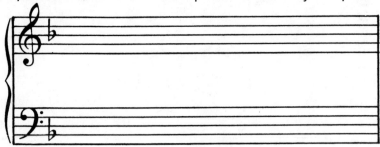

CHORDS (F, Bb, C7)

The three chords of F, Bb, and C7 are used repeatedly in the key of F Major.

4. Draw the following chords. Use dotted half notes. Play these chords.

F   Bb   C7   F

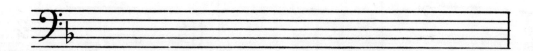

*Refer to page 45 for the complete F Major scale. The manuscript paper on pages 46-48 may be used for practice in writing out this scale.

HARMONIZING MELODIES

5. Write the harmony (chords and pedals) for this melody. Write in a suitable registration. Play this piece.

REGISTRATION
UPPER: _____
LOWER: _____
PEDAL: _____
TREM. or VIB: _____

Clementine

HARMONIZING LEAD LINES

6. Play the following melody with your Right Hand. Play chords and pedals indicated by the chord symbols. If no chord symbol is given in a measure, repeat (hold) the same chord from the measure before.

ELECTRONIC ORGANS
UPPER: Flutes 8′ 4′ (Play 8va)
LOWER: Guitar (Strum) or Diapason 8′
PEDAL: 16′
TREM. and VIB: Off
RHYTHM: Fox trot

DRAWBAR ORGANS
UPPER: 00 8803 000 (Play 8va)
LOWER: (00) 6542 000
PEDAL: 4 3 Spinet 4
VIB: Off
RHYTHM: Fox trot

FOLK SONG

Red River Valley

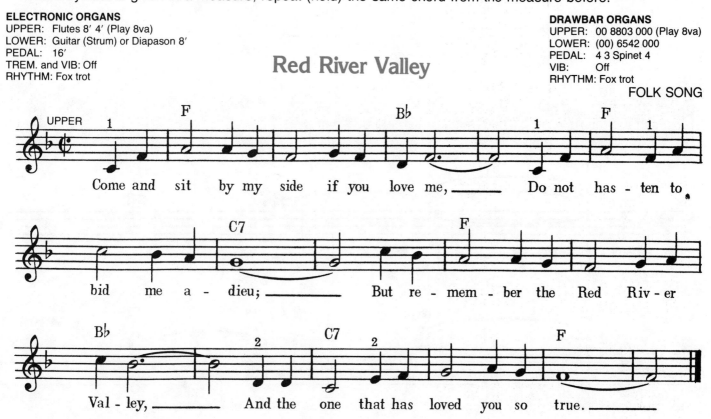

Come and sit by my side if you love me, _____ Do not has - ten to

bid me a - dieu; _____ But re - mem - ber the Red Riv - er

Val - ley, _____ And the one that has loved you so true. _____

WR3   UNIT 7

TECHNIC

F MAJOR SCALE STUDIES

Practice these studies turning the thumb under or crossing over the thumb as smoothly as possible.

Harmonizing the F Major Scale

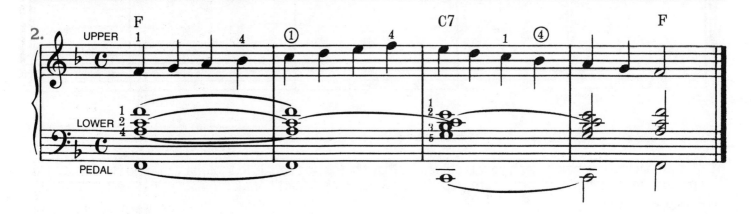

Watch the music while playing these pedal and chord studies.

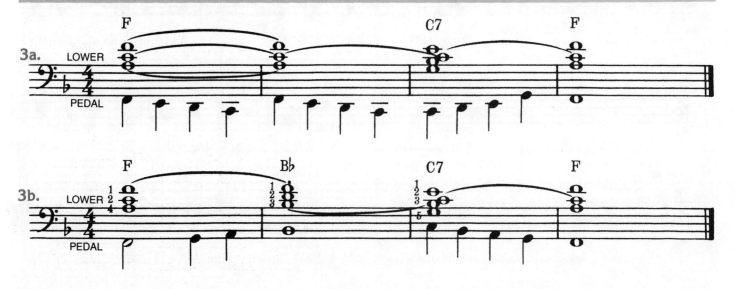

SIGHT READING

*From this point on, write your own registrations for each SIGHT READING piece.

UNIT 8

THEORY

MAJOR AND MINOR CHORDS

Chords are built on scale degrees. The MAJOR TRIAD (3-note chord) built on the 1st tone of the Major scale is formed from the 1st, 3rd, and 5th tones of the scale.

The triad consists of a Root, 3rd, and 5th. The triad is in ROOT POSITION when the 1st tone (Root) is the lowest note.

1. Name and play these Major chords in root position.

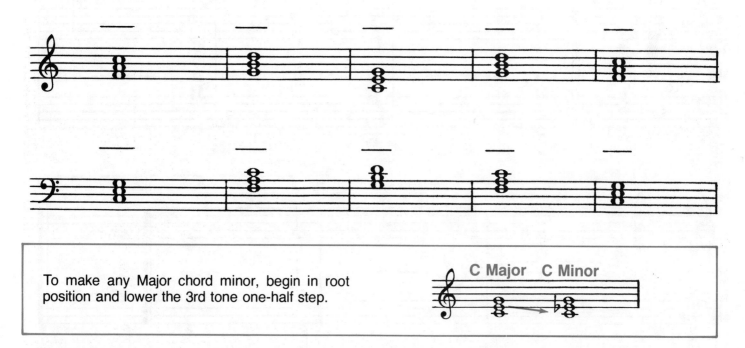

To make any Major chord minor, begin in root position and lower the 3rd tone one-half step.

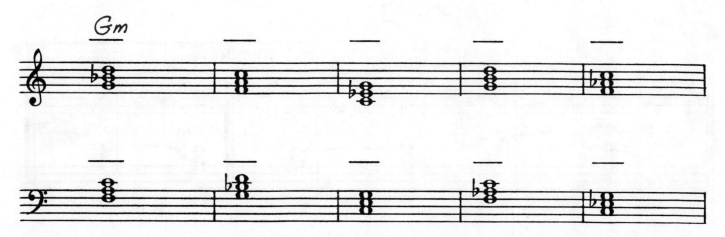

2. Name and play these Major and minor chords in root position. Use a small "m" after the letter when naming minor chords, i.e., Cm.

GROUP 1 KEYS (C, G, F)

The GROUP 1 KEYS are C, G, and F. Each of the I chords is formed in root position with a pattern of "white-white-white" keys.

3. Write the root position I chords in the Group 1 Keys. Play them.

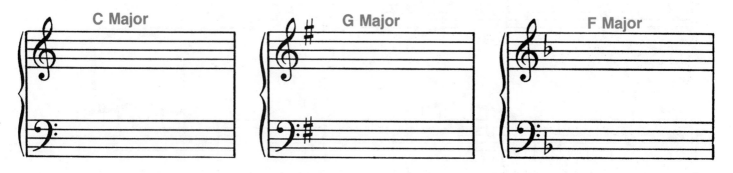

The five finger positions for C and G Major are formed with white keys. F is the unusual key in Group 1, because there is a black key in the five finger position.

4. Write the notes in each five finger position for the Group 1 Keys. Play them.

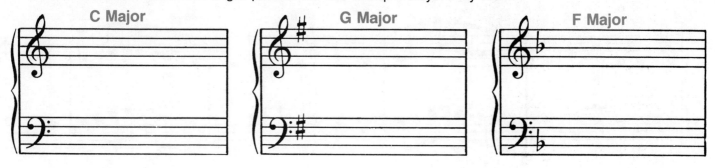

INTERVALS (through the Octave)

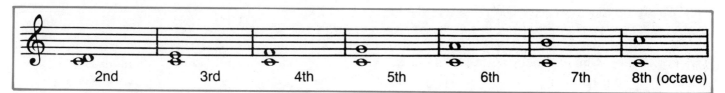

5. Name these harmonic intervals. Play them.

6. Name these melodic intervals. Play them.

TECHNIC

MAJOR-MINOR STUDIES

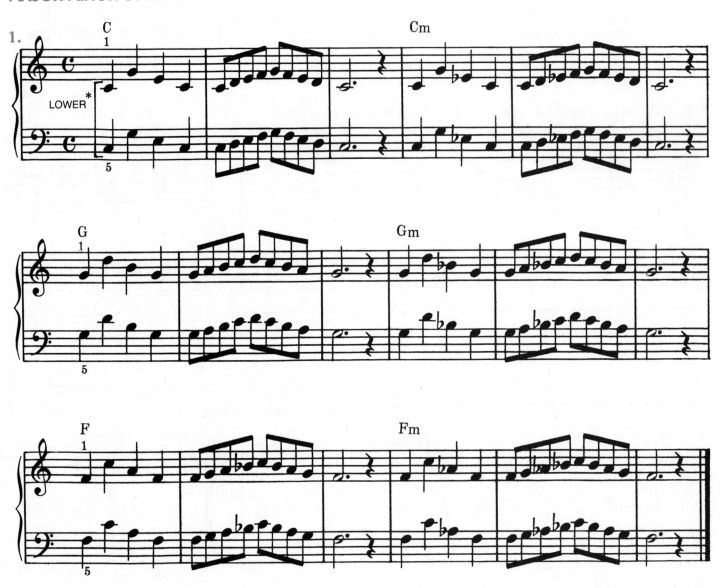

Watch the music while playing these pedal and chord studies.

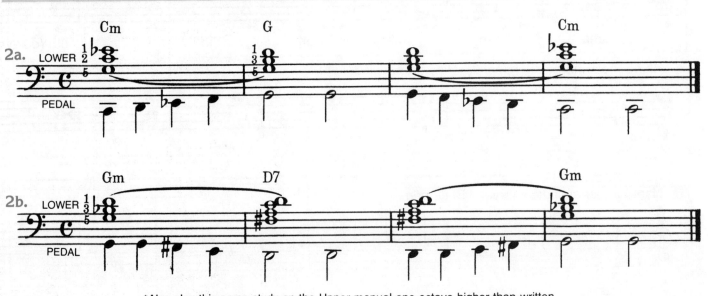

*Also play this same study on the Upper manual one octave higher than written.

UNIT 8   WR3

SIGHT READING

REGISTRATION
UPPER: _____
LOWER: _____
PEDAL: _____
TREM. or VIB: _____

1.

GOD REST YE MERRY GENTLEMEN
(Christmas Song)

REGISTRATION
UPPER: _____
LOWER: _____
PEDAL: _____
TREM. or VIB: _____

2.

BLACK IS THE COLOR OF
MY TRUE LOVE'S HAIR
(Folk Song)

REGISTRATION
UPPER: _____
LOWER: _____
PEDAL: _____
TREM. or VIB: _____

3.

UNIT 9

THEORY

THE ORDER OF SHARPS

The SHARPS are ALWAYS written in this order on the staff.

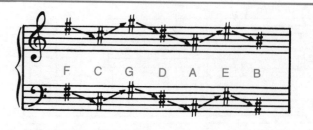

F C G D A E B

1. Write the order of sharps three times on this staff.

MAJOR SHARP KEY SIGNATURES

To find the Major key name of a piece with sharps in the key signature:

1. name the LAST sharp to the right then,

2. name the next letter in the musical alphabet (go up a half step).

   This is the name of the Major key.

C♯   G♯   D♯

D Major   A Major   E Major

2. Name these Major key signatures.

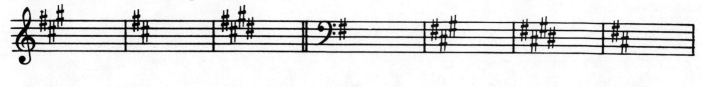

___   ___   ___   ___   ___   ___   ___

___   ___   ___   ___   ___   ___   ___

GROUP 2 KEYS (D, A, E)

> The GROUP 2 KEYS are D, A, and E. Each of the I chords is formed in root position with a pattern of "white-black-white" keys.*

3. Write the root position I chords in the Group 2 Keys. Add the necessary sharps. Play these chords.

> The five finger positions for D and A have only one black key. E is the unusual key in Group 2, because there are two black keys in the five finger position.

4. Write the notes in each five finger position for the Group 2 Keys.** Add the necessary sharps. Play these positions.

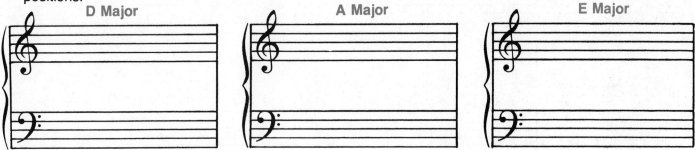

INTERVALS

5. Name the intervals in these melodies. Play them.

*Some organs may have keys of other colors. The black keys referred to here are "sharped" keys.

**Refer to page 45 for the complete scales of D, A, and E Major. The manuscript paper on pages 46-48 may be used for practice in writing these scales.

TECHNIC

HARMONIZING THE SCALES OF D, A, E

Practice each scale separately. Then practice the accompaniment separately. Finally, play each exercise as written.

D MAJOR SCALE

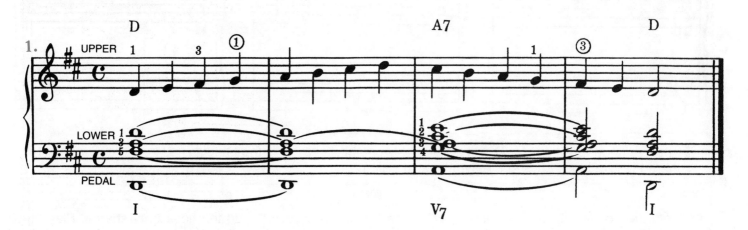

A MAJOR SCALE

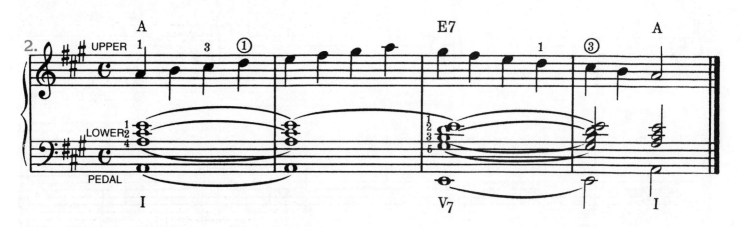

E MAJOR SCALE

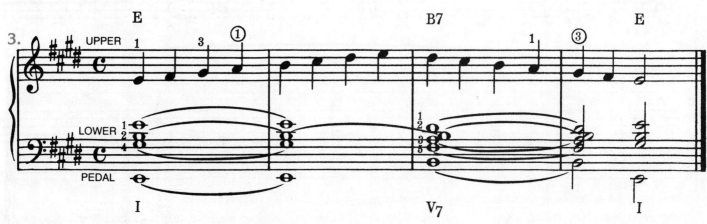

SIGHT READING

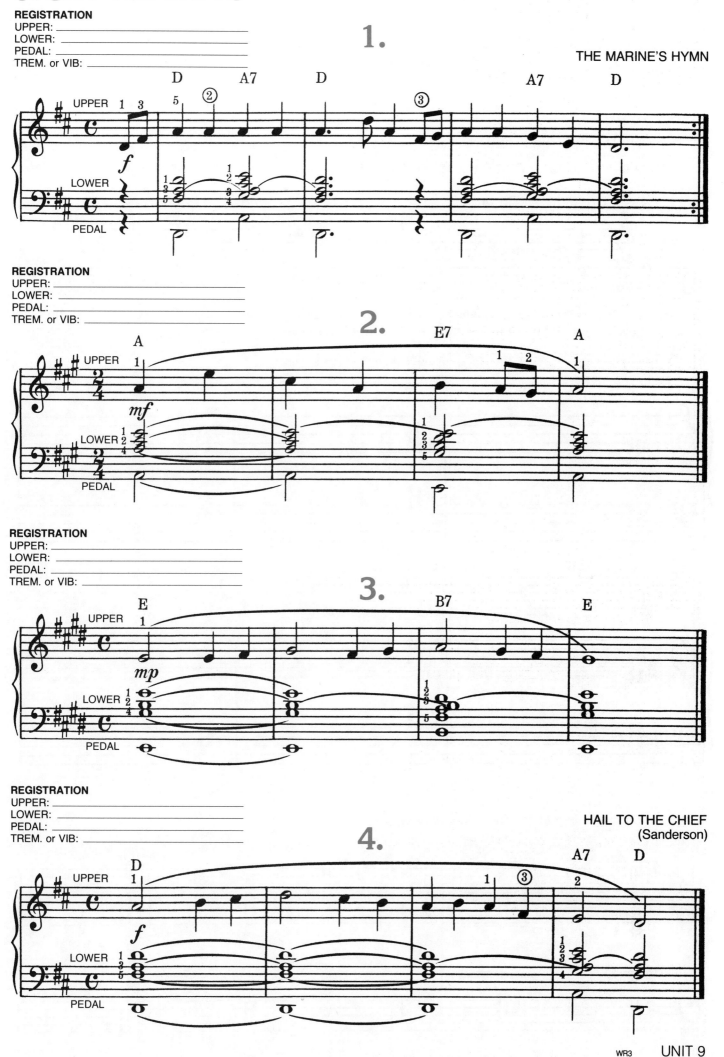

UNIT 10

THEORY

MINOR CHORDS

To write a minor chord, LOWER the MIDDLE NOTE of a Major chord ONE HALF STEP.

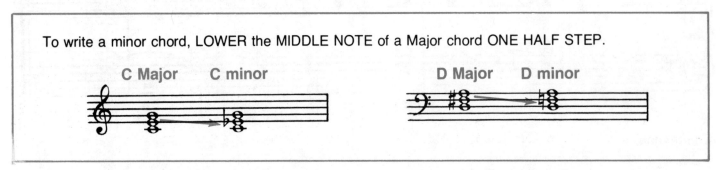

1. After each Major chord, write a minor chord. When you lower the middle note, DO NOT change the letter name. Lower a natural to a FLAT. Lower a sharp to a NATURAL. Play these chords.

GROUP 1 KEYS

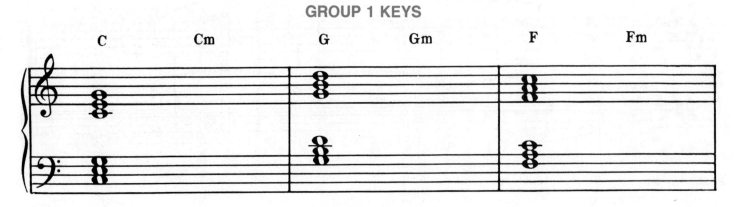

GROUP 2 KEYS

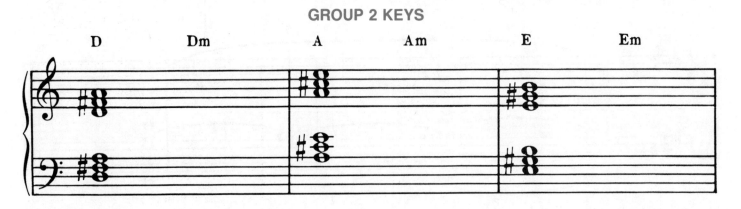

2. Name and play these Major and minor chords.

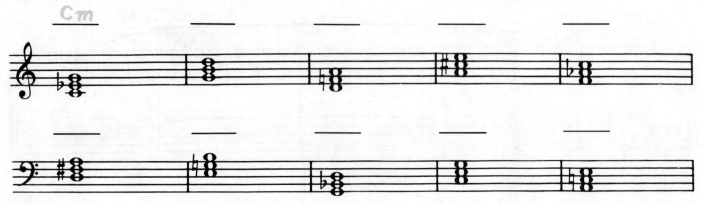

HARMONIZING LEAD LINES

3. Play the following melodies with your Right Hand. Play chords and pedals indicated by the chord symbols. If no chord symbol is given in a measure, repeat (hold) the same chord from the measure before.

ELECTRONIC ORGANS
UPPER: Flutes 8′ 4′ (Play 8va)
LOWER: Guitar (Strum) or Diapason 8′
PEDAL: 16′
TREM. and VIB: Off
RHYTHM: Fox Trot

DRAWBAR ORGANS
UPPER: 00 8803 000 (Play 8va)
LOWER: (00) 6542 000
PEDAL: 4 3 Spinet 4
VIB: Off
RHYTHM: Fox Trot

She'll Be Comin' 'Round the Mountain

AMERICAN FOLK SONG

ELECTRONIC ORGANS
UPPER: Strings 8′ 4′
LOWER: Tibia 8′
PEDAL: 16′
TREM: Off
VIB: On (Light or Delay)
RHYTHM: Waltz 3/4

DRAWBAR ORGANS
UPPER: 00 3676 532
LOWER: (00) 4321 000
PEDAL: 2 2 Spinet 2
VIB: Delay
RHYTHM: Waltz 3/4

The Ash Grove

WELSH FOLK SONG

WR3 UNIT 10

TECHNIC

STUDIES IN MINOR

Practice each melody separately. Then practice the accompaniment separately. Finally, play each exercise as written.

1.

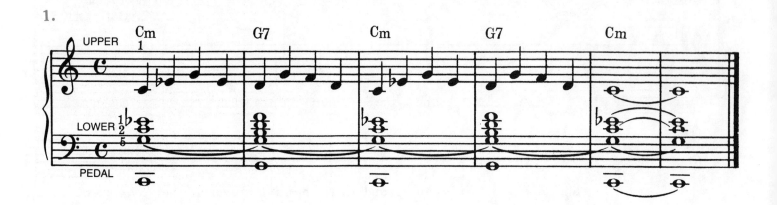

2.

3.

Watch the music while playing this pedal and chord study.

4.

SIGHT READING

REGISTRATION
UPPER: _____
LOWER: _____
PEDAL: _____
TREM. or VIB: _____

1.

GO DOWN, MOSES
(Spiritual)

REGISTRATION
UPPER: _____
LOWER: _____
PEDAL: _____
TREM. or VIB: _____

2.

REGISTRATION
UPPER: _____
LOWER: _____
PEDAL: _____
TREM. or VIB: _____

3.

THE ERIE CANAL
(Allen)

REFERENCE

PRIMARY CHORDS — I, IV, V7

Chords are labeled with Roman numerals to indicate the degree of the scale on which each chord is formed.

The PRIMARY CHORDS are built on the 1st, 4th, and 5th degrees of the scale. Each scale degree has a name. The primary chord names are:

I - TONIC   IV - SUB-DOMINANT   V - DOMINANT

V7 CHORD

You have played both the V and the V7 chord (DOMINANT SEVENTH). The dominant seventh is a 4-note chord. It is formed in root position by adding another note above the V chord. The V7 chord has a Root and the intervals of a 3rd, 5th, and 7th.

KEY OF C MAJOR (I-C)

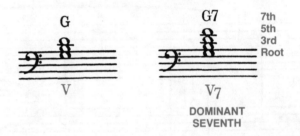

V7 CHORD — INVERTED

You have played the V7 chord in root position and in inverted (rearranged) positions. (The inverted V7 chords shown here are used for a better sound on the organ.)

KEY OF G MAJOR

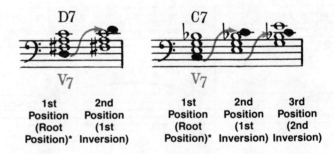

KEY OF D MAJOR

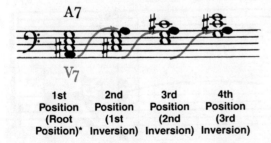

KEY OF A MAJOR

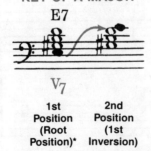

KEY OF E MAJOR

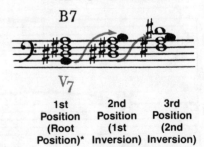

*These terms may be used interchangeably.

MAJOR SCALES AND PRIMARY CHORDS (Group 1 and 2 Keys)

MANUSCRIPT PAPER

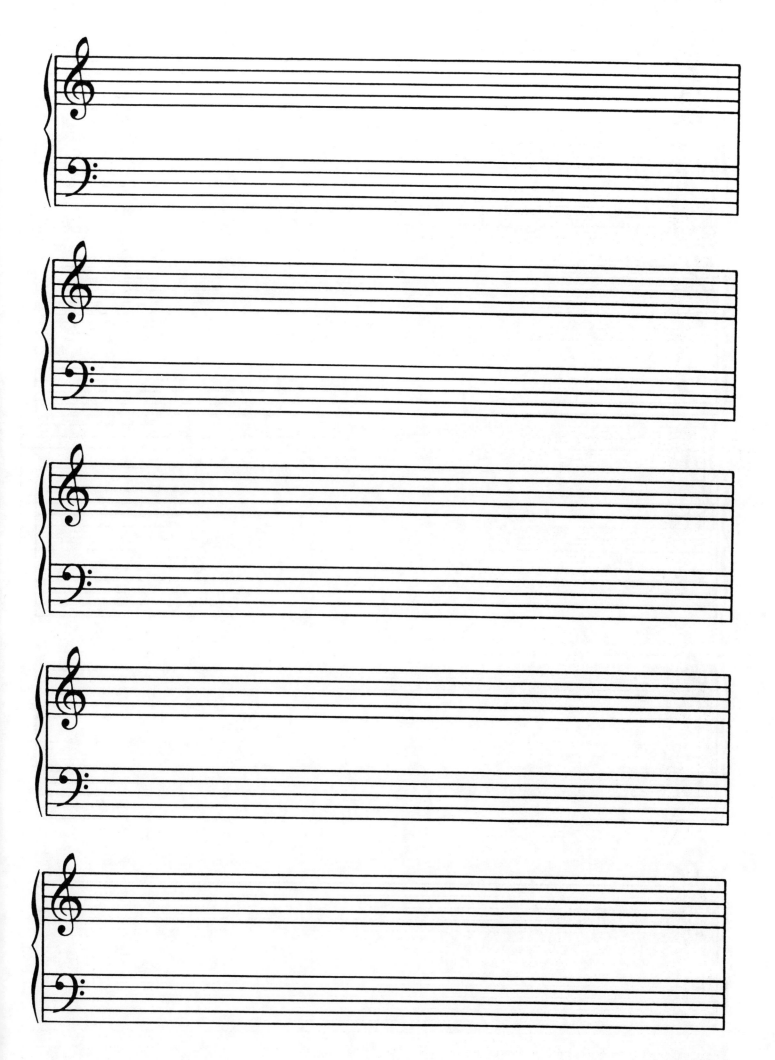

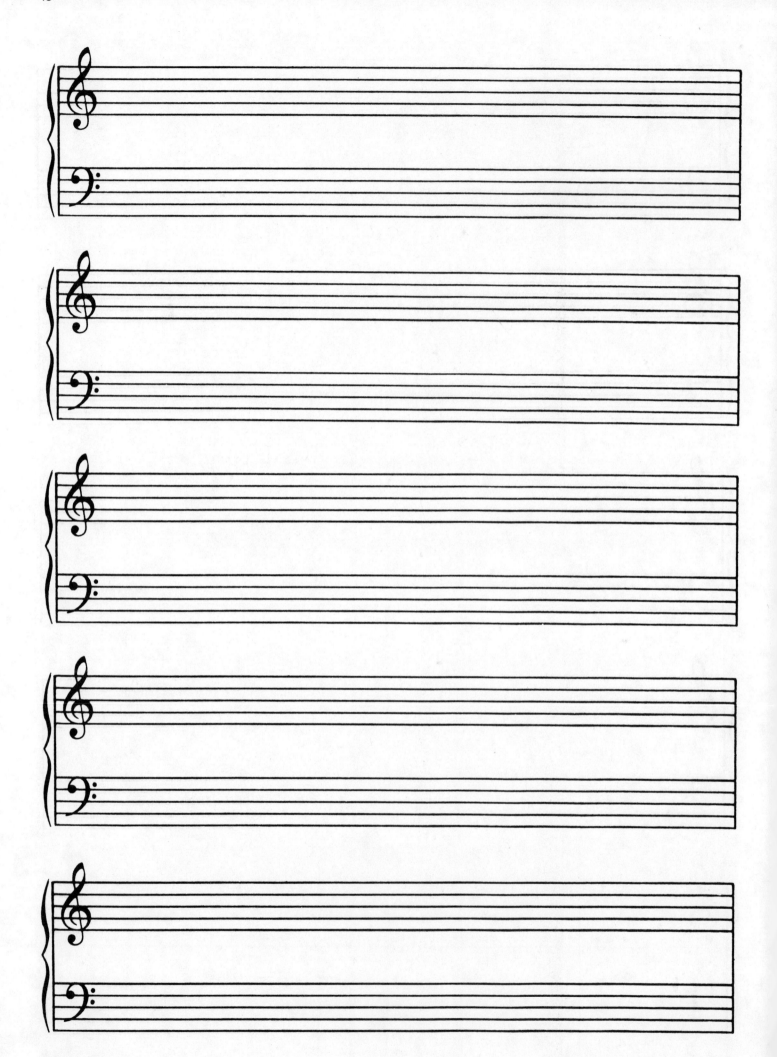